# Sports Themes

Wise Publications
London/New York/Paris/Sydney/
Copenhagen/Madrid

Exclusive Distributors:
**Music Sales Limited**
8/9 Frith Street, London W1V 5TZ, England.
**Music Sales Pty Limited**
120 Rothschild Avenue, Rosebery, NSW 2018, Australia.

Order No. AM955317
ISBN 0-7119-7436-5
This book © Copyright 1999 by Wise Publications

Compiled by Nick Crispin
Music arranged by Stephen Duro
Music processed by Allegro Reproductions
Cover photograph courtesy of Richard Sellers/Sportsphoto

Printed in the United Kingdom by
Halstan & Co Limited, Amersham, Buckinghamshire.

**Your Guarantee of Quality**
As publishers, we strive to produce every book to the highest commercial standards.
The music has been freshly engraved and the book has been carefully designed to minimise
awkward page turns and to make playing from it a real pleasure.
Particular care has been given to specifying acid-free, neutral-sized paper made from pulps
which have not been elemental chlorine bleached. This pulp is from farmed sustainable forests
and was produced with special regard for the environment.
Throughout, the printing and binding have been planned to ensure a sturdy, attractive publication
which should give years of enjoyment.
If your copy fails to meet our high standards, please inform us and we will gladly replace it.

Music Sales' complete catalogue describes thousands of titles and is available in full colour sections
by subject, direct from Music Sales Limited. Please state your areas of interest
and send a cheque/postal order for £1.50 for postage to:
Music Sales Limited, Newmarket Road, Bury St. Edmunds, Suffolk IP33 3YB.

www.internetmusicshop.com

# A Musical Joke
## (BBC Horse Of The Year Show)
### Composed by Wolfgang Amadeus Mozart

# Carnaval de Paris
## (World Cup '98)

By Paul Spencer, Stephen Spencer & Scott Rosser

**Moderately bright**

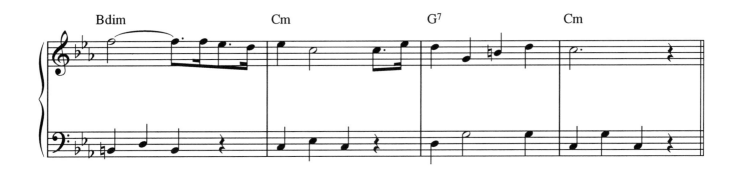

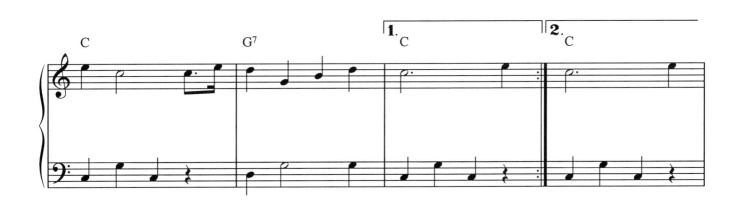

# Challenge
## (BBC Sports Personality Of The Year)
### By Charles Williams

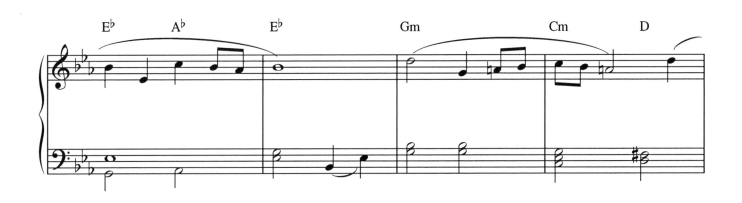

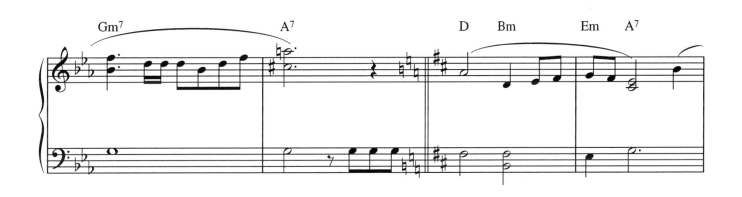

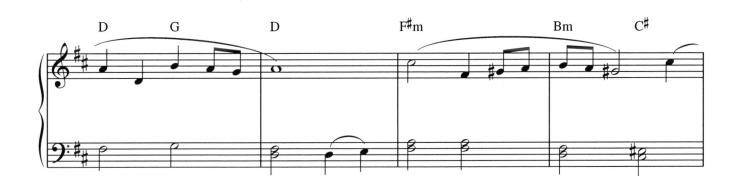

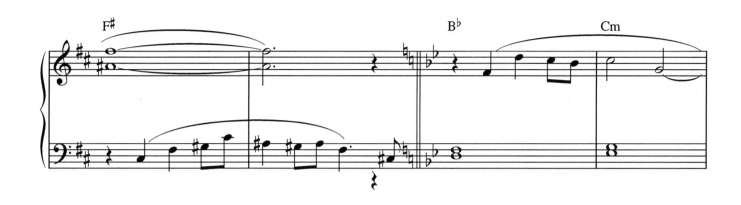

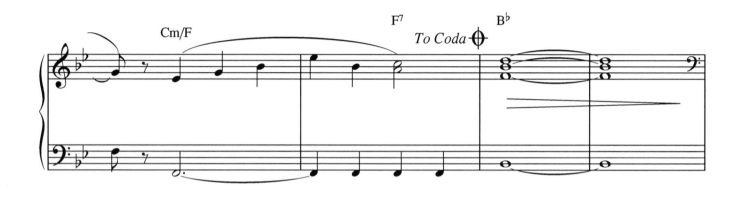

# Don't Come Home Too Soon
## (Scotland's World Cup '98 Theme)
### Words & Music by Justin Currie

**Moderately slow**

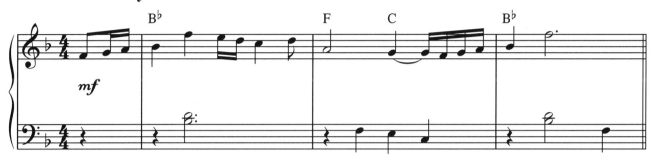

So long, go on and do your best, let all France have whis-key on its breath, the

world may not be sha-kin' yet but you might prove them wrong, ev - en long shots make

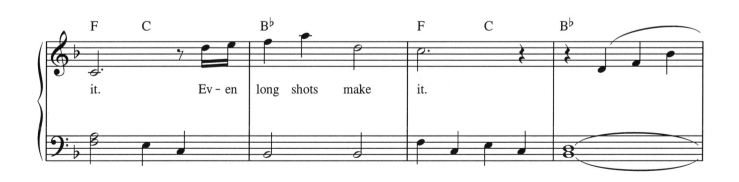

it. Ev - en long shots make it.

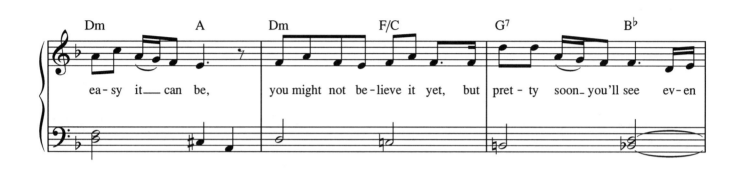

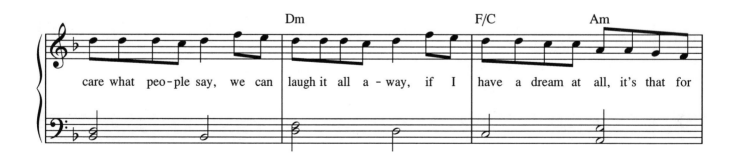

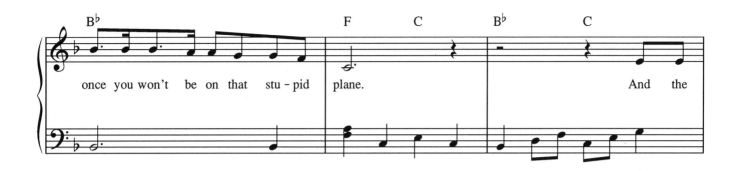

once you won't be on that stu - pid plane. And the

world may not be shak - in' yet, but you might prove— them wrong, ev - en

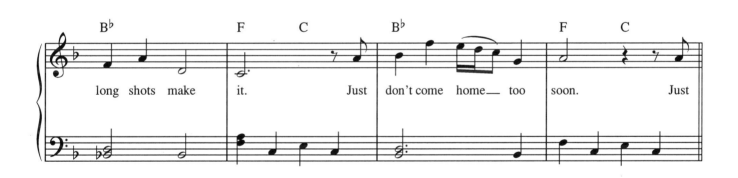

long shots make it. Just don't come home— too soon. Just

*Repeat & Fade*

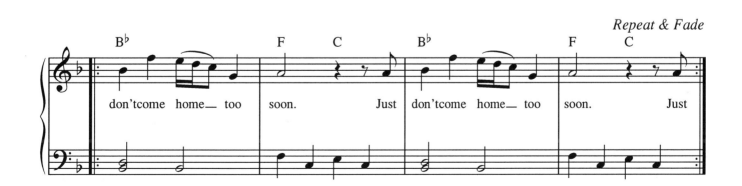

don'tcome home— too soon. Just don'tcome home— too soon. Just

# Grandstand

## By Keith Mansfield

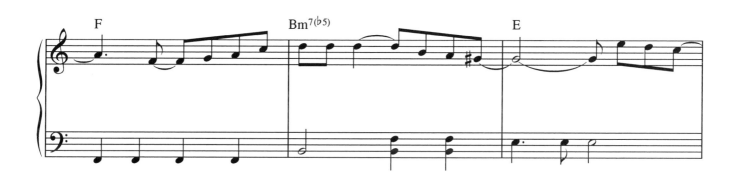

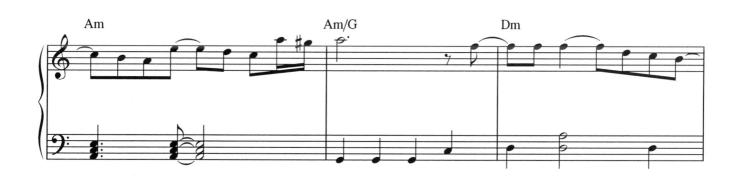

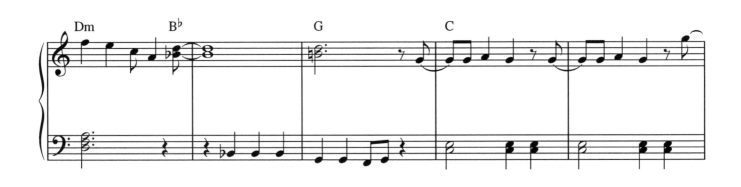

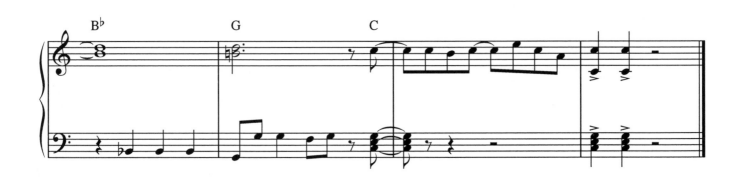

# Jerusalem

## (ITV Euro '96)

**Music by Hubert Parry**
**Words by William Blake**

**Moderately with breadth**

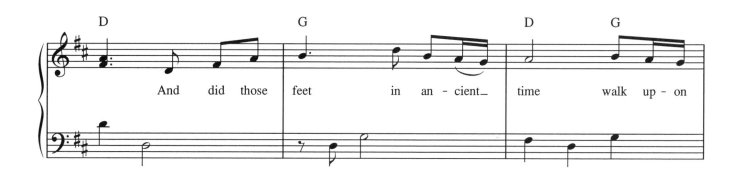

And did those feet in an-cient— time walk up-on

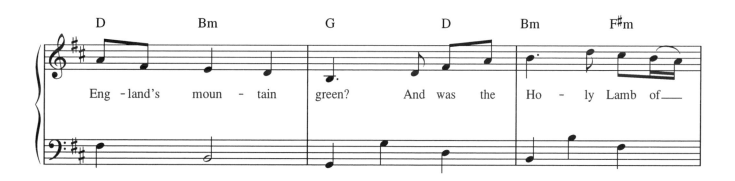

Eng-land's moun - tain green? And was the Ho - ly Lamb of—

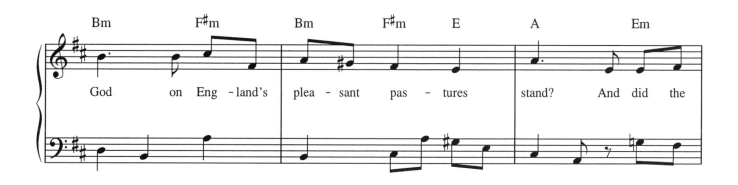

God on Eng-land's plea - sant pas - tures stand? And did the

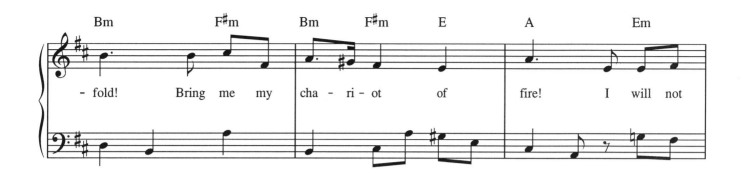

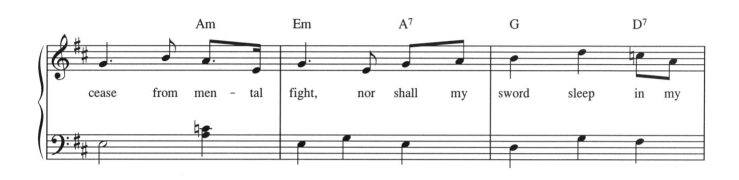

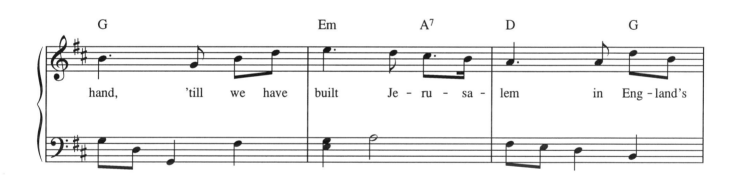

# Light And Tuneful
## (Wimbledon Opening Theme)
**By Keith Mansfield**

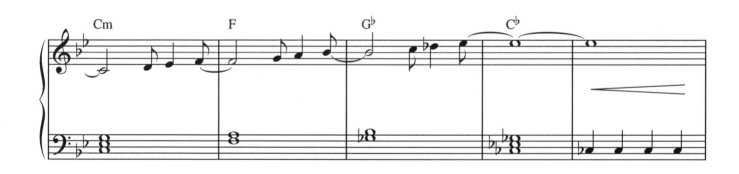

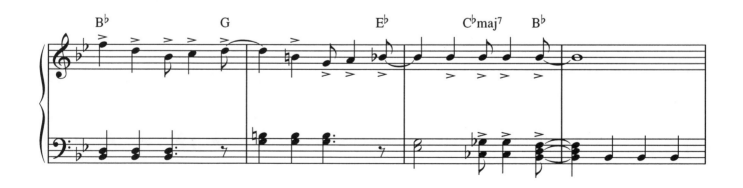

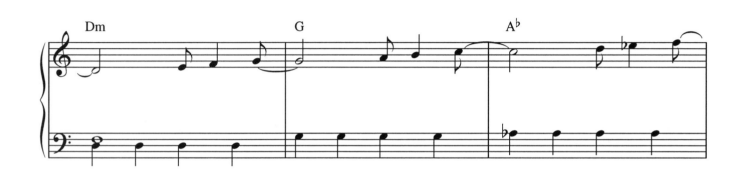

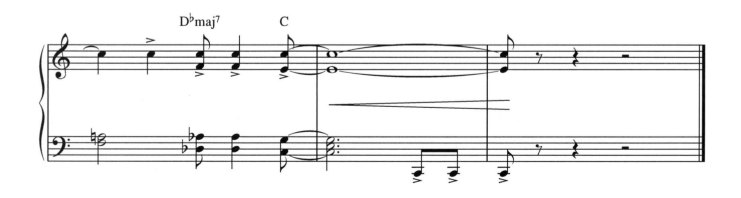

# Nessun Dorma from Turandot
## (BBC World Cup '90)
### By Giacomo Puccini

**Moderately**

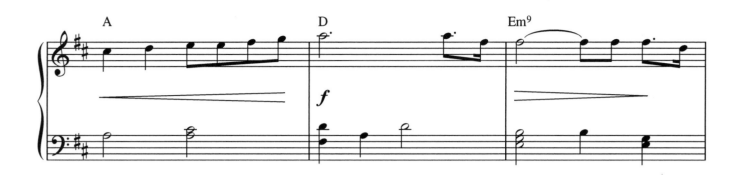

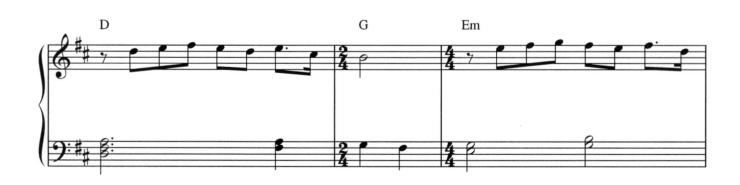

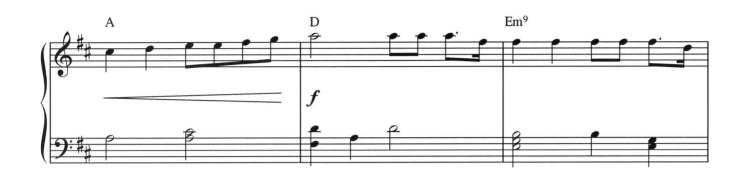

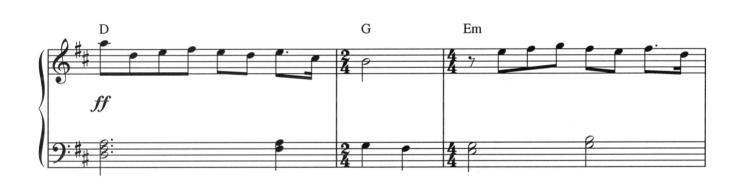

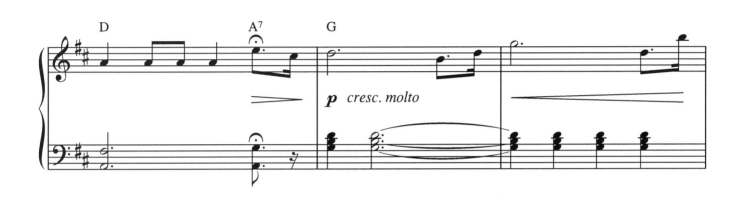

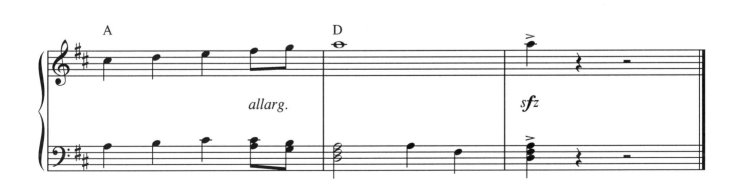

# Pavane

## (BBC World Cup '98)

**Composed by Gabriel Fauré, words by Robert de Montesquiou**
**Arranged by Elizabeth Parker**

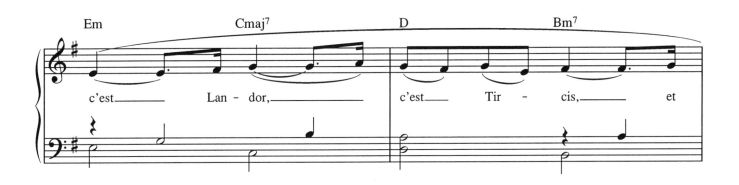

c'est_____ Lan - dor,_____ c'est_____ Tir - cis,_____ et

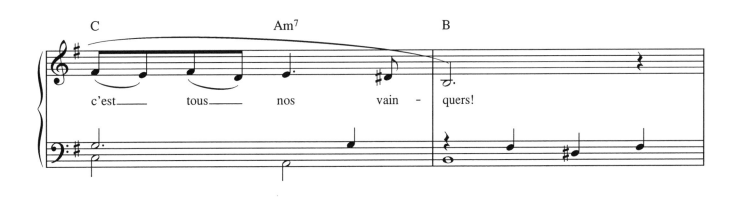

c'est_____ tous_____ nos vain - quers!

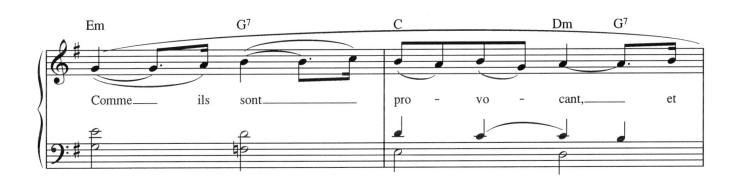

Comme_____ ils sont_____ pro - vo - cant,_____ et

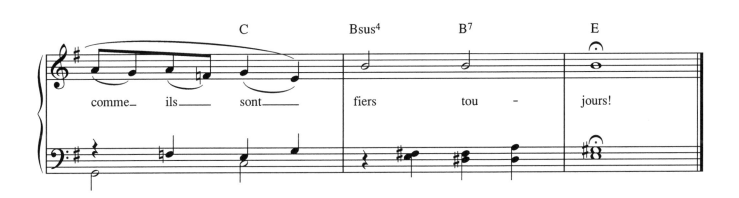

comme_____ ils_____ sont_____ fiers tou - jours!

# Ode To Joy from Symphony No. 9
## (BBC Euro '96)
### Composed by Ludwig van Beethoven

**With movement**

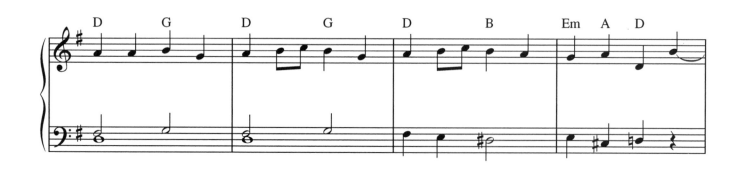

# Ski Sunday Theme (Pop Looks Bach)

**By Sam Fonteyn**

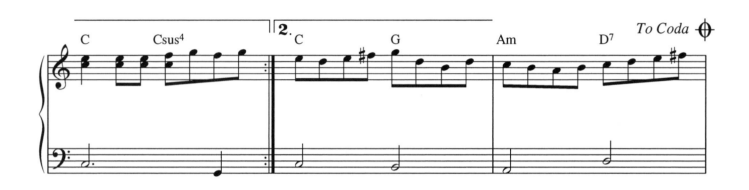

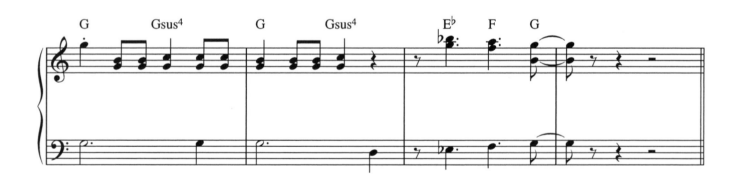

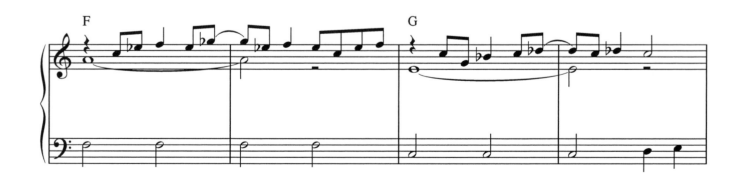

*D.S. al Coda*

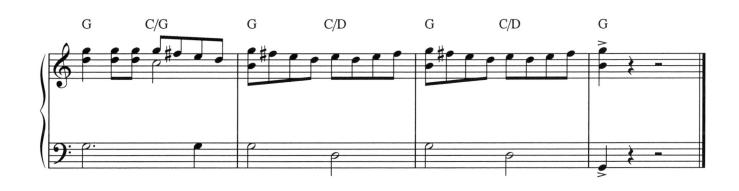

# Swing Low, Sweet Chariot
## (Rugby Anthem)
### Traditional

**Slowly**

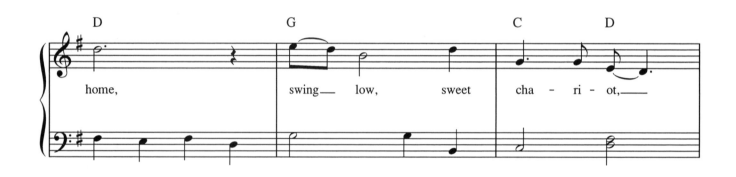

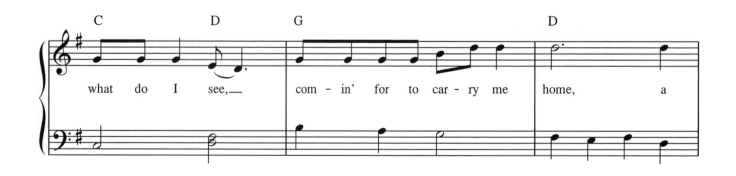

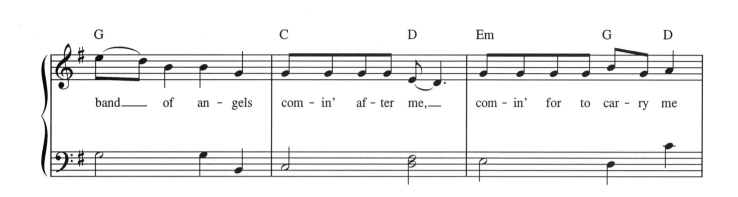

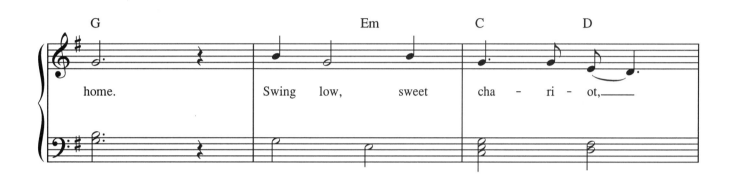

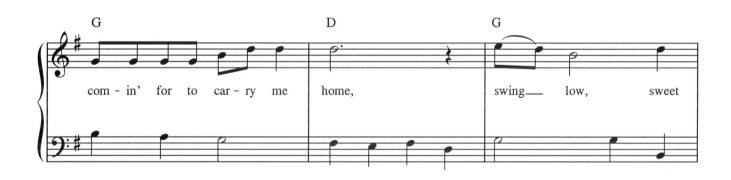

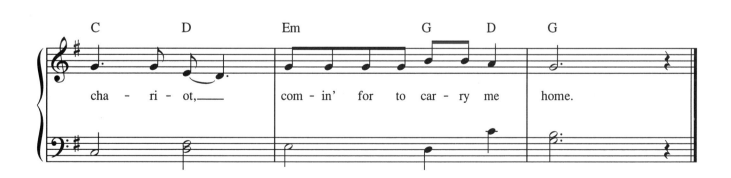

# Sportsnight Theme

**By Tony Hatch**

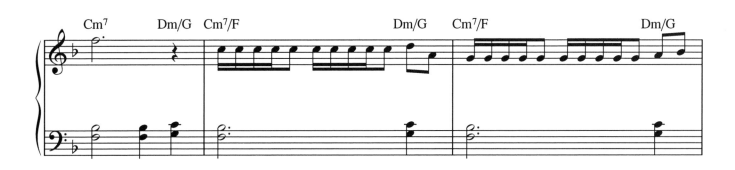

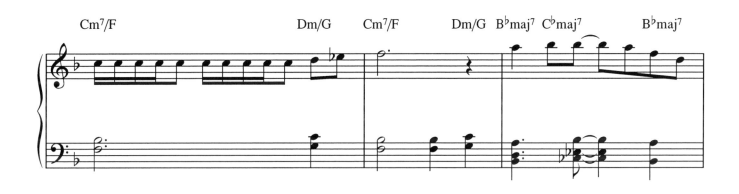

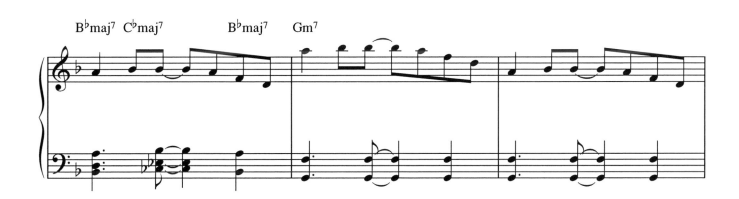

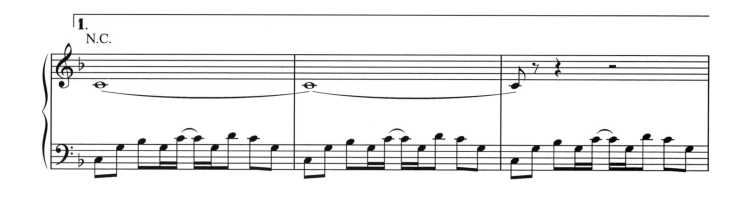

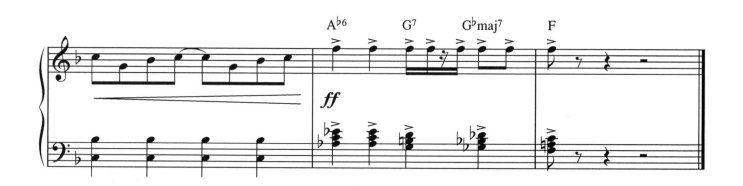

# The Trap
## (The London Marathon)
### By Ron Goodwin

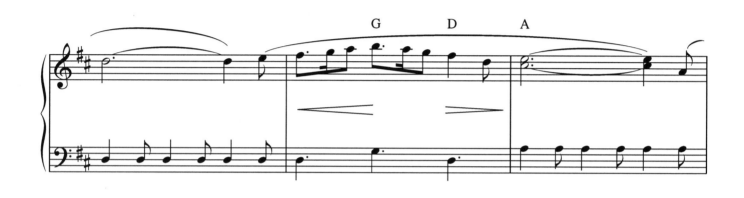

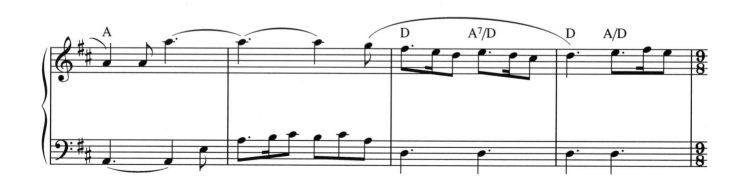

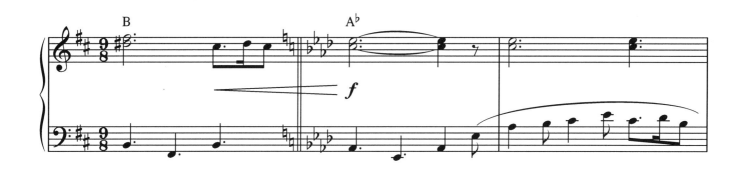

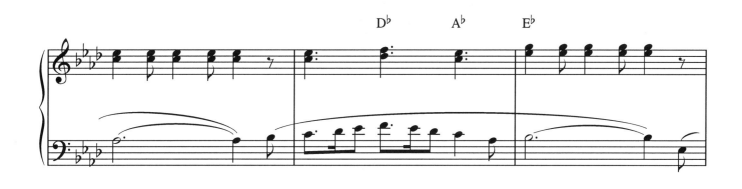

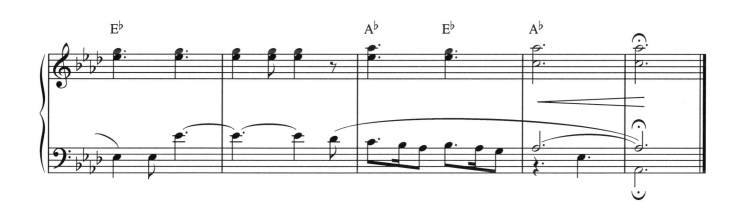

# World In Union
## (World Cup Rugby 1991)

**By Gustav Holst**
**Arranged by Charlie Skarbek**

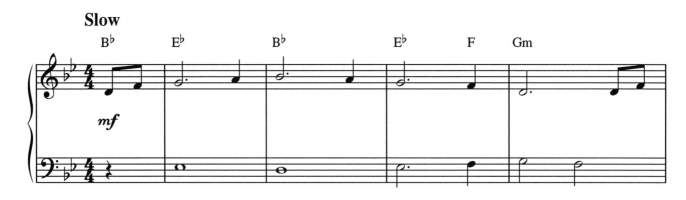

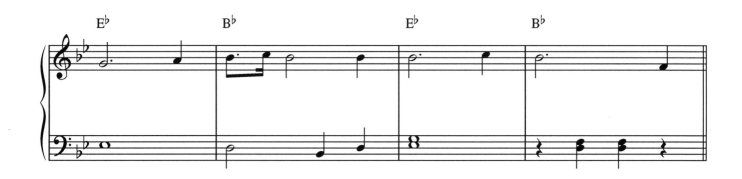

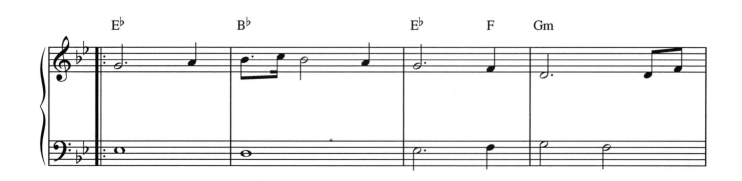

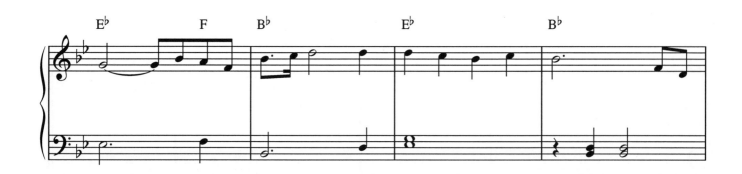

# You'll Never Walk Alone

## (Football Anthem)

**Music by Richard Rodgers**
**Words by Oscar Hammerstein II**

**With warmth, like a hymn**

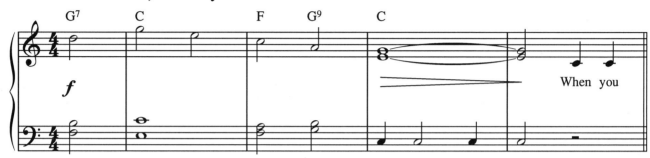

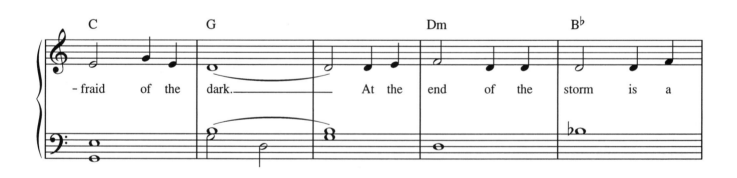

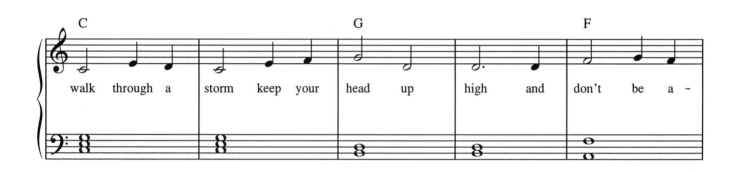

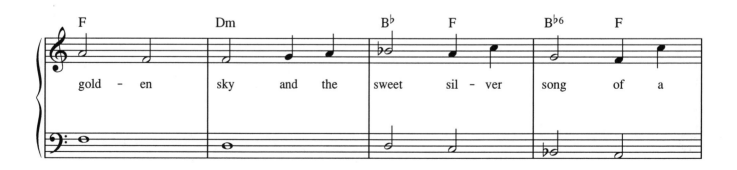

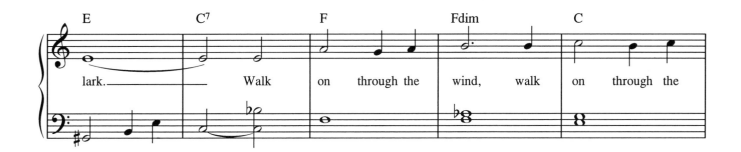

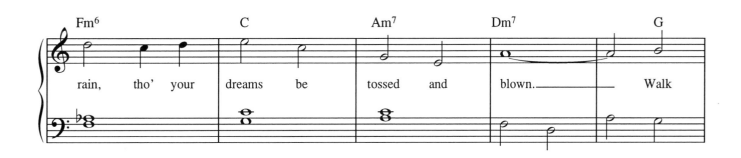

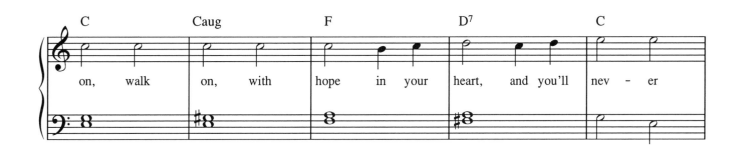

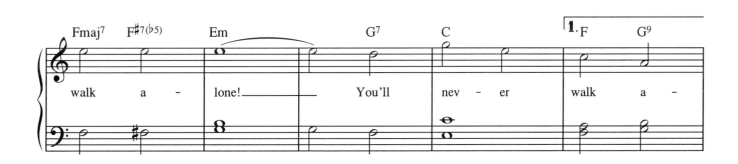

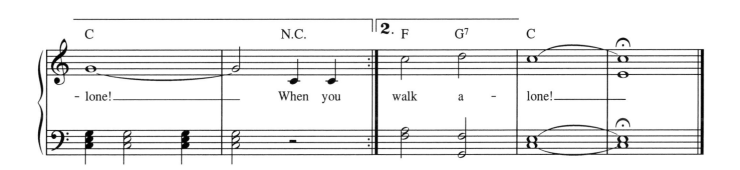

# Three Lions '98
## (World Cup '98)
**Music by Ian Broudie**
**Words by David Baddiel & Frank Skinner**

**Moderately**

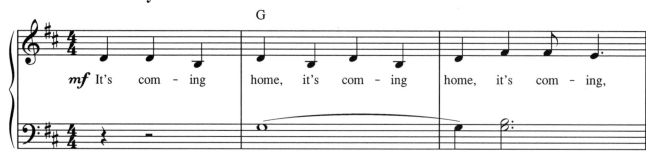

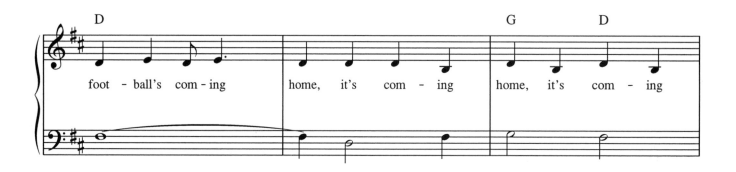

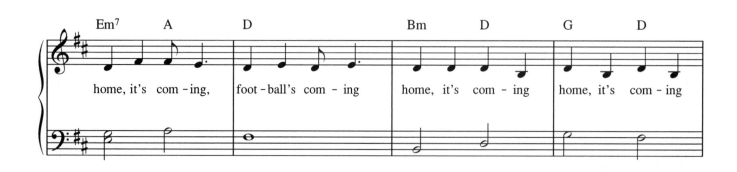

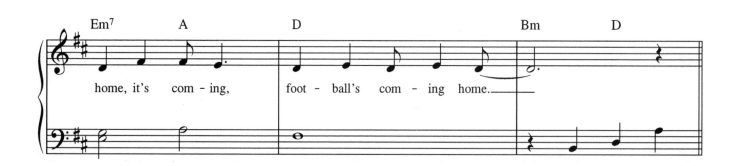

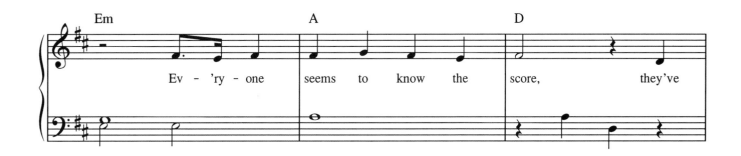

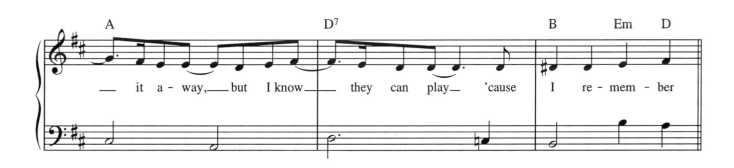

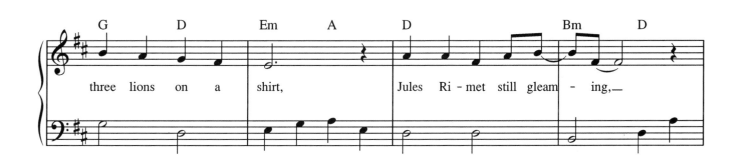

thir - ty years of hurt, nev - er stopped me dream - ing.

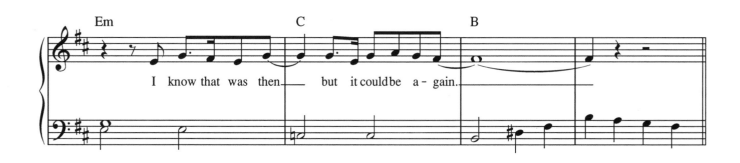

I know that was then but it could be a - gain.

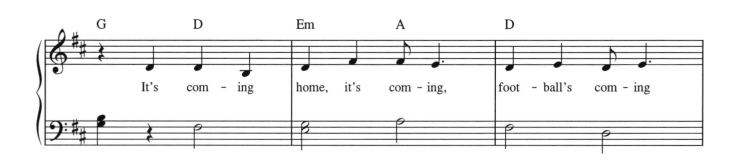

It's com - ing home, it's com - ing, foot - ball's com - ing

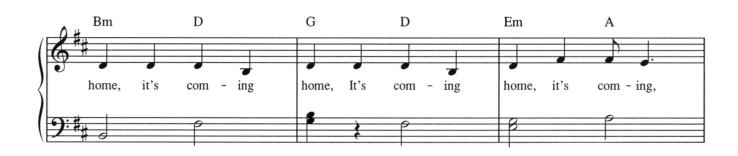

home, it's com - ing home, It's com - ing home, it's com - ing,

foot - ball's com - ing home, it's com - ing home.